MW00785069

This is a work of satire, parody, commentary, critique and fiction. Names, characters, places and incidents are either the product of the author's imagination, are used fictitiously or as satire, parody, commentary and critique. Any resemblance to real world events is purely coincidental.

Copyright © 2020 by Joshua William Montgomery

All rights reserved. No part of this book may be reproduced or used in any manner without written permission of the copyright owner except for the use of quotations in a book review.

First edition February 2021

ISBN 978-1-7365133-0-9

This book is dedicated to the Electronic Frontier Foundation and Unified Patents – knights in armor fighting trolls for people like you and me.

Once upon a time there were three children named Dunker, Jasmine and Lee.

All three of them respected their teachers, studied hard and got to go to a special school where they learned how to create golden papers called patents.

A patent is a special paper stamped by the King that helps inventors take ideas and make them real.

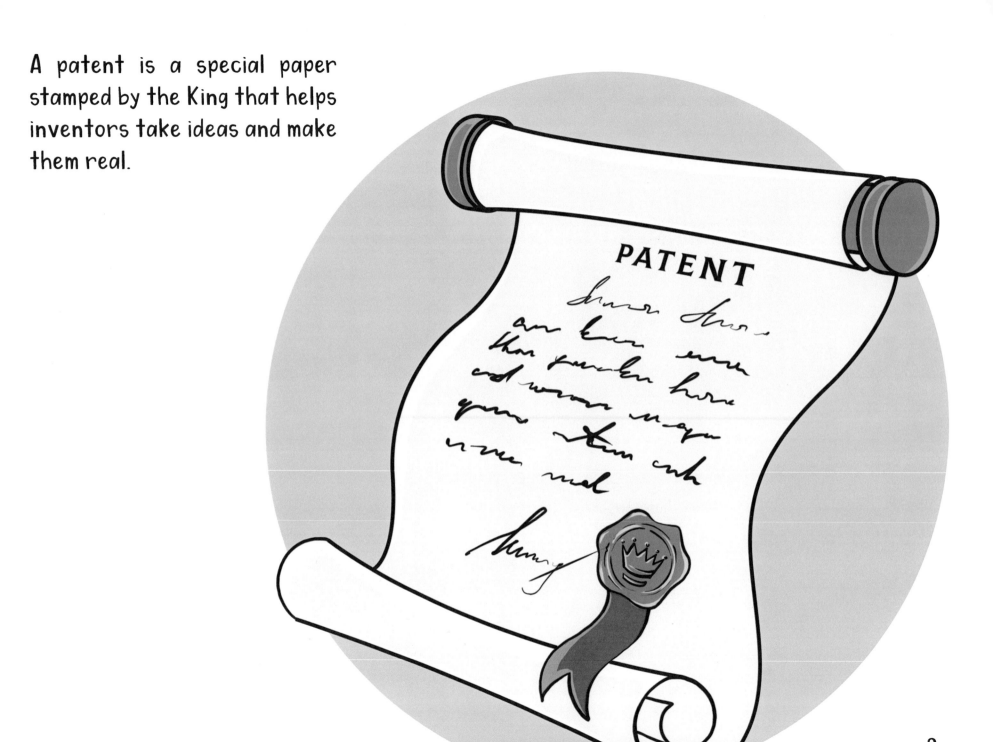

Of course only the best, most useful, greatest and inventive ideas are supposed to become patents.

4

But Dunker and Jasmine discovered that the examiners were too busy to check on each and every idea.

So they took some obvious ideas and tricked the examiners into stamping them for the King.

Examiner

7

"We don't need to have new ideas." said Dunker. "We can patent old ideas and use them to make people give us their gold."

8

Dunker and Jasmine spent so much time scheming for gold that soon they became ugly. Their backs grew bent, they grew warts on their noses and they began to smell.

They became so ugly and smelly that the townsfolk made them leave. So they took their evil patents and moved under a bridge and became trolls.

Meanwhile, Lee was working hard to help people with good ideas to make inventions.

"That is a great idea," said Lee to Farmer Josh. "Your invention will help chickens lay bigger eggs and feed more people!"

Since Lee spent his time helping people he grew stronger and taller and more handsome.

He worked so hard helping people that soon he was able to buy the shining armor he had always wanted.

One day, Lee's friend Mycroft went for a walk and had a great idea.

He ran toward Lee's house to tell him, but as he crossed the bridge Dunker and Jasmine jumped out in front of him.

"That is our idea," said Jasmine. "We have a patent granted by the King. Give us your gold or we'll tell the King and he will put you in jail for stealing our idea."

14

Mycroft was concerned. Did these trolls really have a patent on his idea?

He looked at their patent and read it carefully.

"This patent doesn't have anything to do with my idea," said Mycroft. "Your idea is a bad idea that should never have been patented at all!"

But Dunker and Jasmine did not listen.

They washed off their stink, put on disguises and started walking toward the castle to tell the king.

16

Poor Mycroft didn't know what to do.

Even though the troll's patents were bad they had the King's stamp. What would happen if the King believed the trolls?

When Mycroft told Lee what happened he got his friends Michael, Chris, Jean, Hissan and Justin and they climbed on their horses and raced to the castle.

Just as the trolls were about to trick the King into sending soldiers to arrest Mycroft, Lee and the knights burst into the throne room.

"Stop!" said Lee. "These trolls are liars!"

19

No one had ever challenged the trolls before. They were so surprised that they tripped and fell and their disguises came off.

Seeing the trolls for what they were, the King took their patent and tore it up.

"How dare you abuse patents to steal other people's gold." said the King. "Take these trolls to the dungeon!"

Just then, Farmer Josh walked into the chamber with a giant egg.

"It works!" shouted Farmer Josh. "My invention helps chickens lay beautiful giant eggs!"

"What is it called?" asked the King.

"I call it NewEgg," said Farmer Josh and everyone agreed that it was a great name.

So the King invited Mycroft and Lee and the knights and Farmer Josh to a big feast to celebrate NewEgg and the defeat of the patent trolls.

And what happened to the trolls?

Well, that was very unfortunate.

The next morning the sun
shined into their cell.

And in the light of day they melted and ran down the drain.

Until the only thing left to remind the honest citizens of the kingdom that the trolls ever existed....

26

...was their stench.

27

About the Author

Joshua Montgomery is an entrepreneur who believes people can build technology without becoming evil. He lives under the benevolent dictatorship of a cat named Crookshanks in Holualoa Hawaii with his wife & co-founder Kris Adair, their daughters Audrey and Maurene and a fierce toy poodle named Cujo.

CPSIA information can be obtained
at www.ICGtesting.com
Printed in the USA
LVRC102150270122
709615LV00001B/1